Story Po

GW00986199

Selected by Wendy Body

Contents

LONGMAN

A Song About Myself

There was a naughty boy,
A naughty boy was he,
He would not stop at home,
He could not quiet be –
He took
In his knapsack
A book
Full of vowels
And a shirt
With some towels –

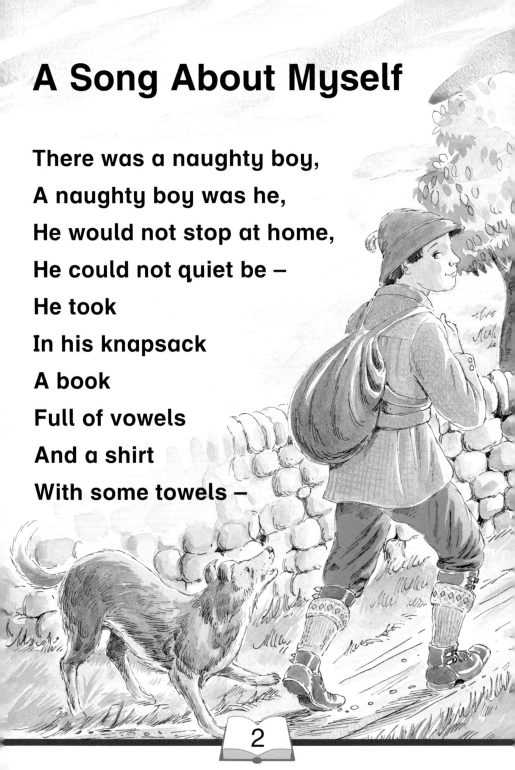

A slight cap
For a night-cap –
A hair brush,
Comb ditto,
New stockings,
For old ones
Would split O!
This knapsack
Tight at's back
He rivetted close
And followed his nose
To the North,
To the North,
And followed his nose
To the North.

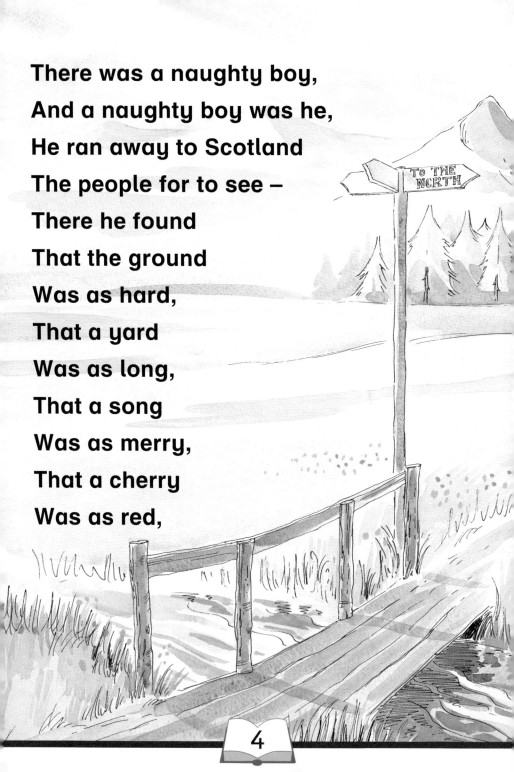

There was a naughty boy,
And a naughty boy was he,
He ran away to Scotland
The people for to see –
There he found
That the ground
Was as hard,
That a yard
Was as long,
That a song
Was as merry,
That a cherry
Was as red,

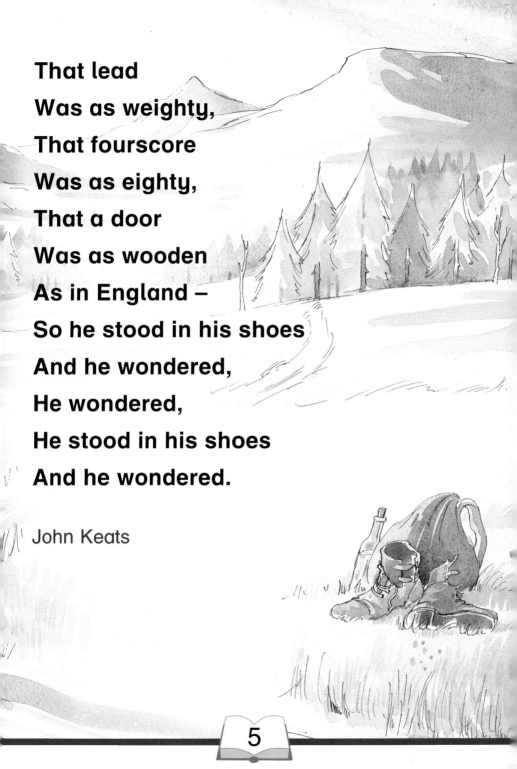

That lead

Was as weighty,

That fourscore

Was as eighty,

That a door

Was as wooden

As in England –

So he stood in his shoes

And he wondered,

He wondered,

He stood in his shoes

And he wondered.

John Keats

Jack's Tale

'At day-break, Jack finding the Giant not likely to be soon roused, crept softly out of his hiding-place, seized the hen, and ran off with her.'

Iona and Peter Opie: *The Classic Fairy Tales*

Sun rises before me,
dazzles pathless flight.
In the corner of each eye
mists drift and fade,
dissolve against a lightening sky;
the tops of oaks sprawl
like giant undergrowth below.
I dare not pause to gaze,
I dare not fall!

Behind, as if in smoke,
the castle disappears.
My life is ruled by noise:
heart drums inside my chest,
the giant thud of angry steps
invades my ears.

Beneath one arm
a squirming weight of feathers,
crooked between waist and elbow,
squawks our whereabouts into the dawn;
scratches tales of panic into flesh.
All thoughts are on escape;
all golden dreams have flown!

Ahead, at last,
green stalks emerge from cloud
then cobweb downwards,
stitching earth to sky.
I leap, grasp branches urgently
with outstretched hand;
half-slide, half-fall
to blessed earth below,
to blessed land.

Judith Nicholls

Hayley Muffet – Spider Woman

Hayley loved spiders, she'd a thousand
at least,
From tiniest ticklers to great hairy beasts.
A gang of black widows spun webs on
her head
And tarantulas slept at the end
of her bed.

She's trained all her spiders
    to do crafty tricks,
They'd jump out on the milkman and
    chase him with sticks –
The bird-eating spiders had windows
    all manned
To machine-gun the pigeons that came
    in to land.

Now none of her neighbours thought
    spiders were fun,
So they wrote to the council, "Now what
    can be done?
Send in the Rentokil man with his spray,
Do anything – just make these pests
    go away."

But the spiders were ready with
    gasmasks in place,
And short-wave transmitters to report
    back to base;
When the man from the council pulled
    up in his van
They leapt from the bushes and battle
    began.

He hadn't a chance. He knew he was beat
When they pulled off his trainers and
    tickled his feet.
They said, "Tell the world that we
    spiders are boss,"
Which made the pest officer
    frightfully cross.

Now Hayley was thrilled with her
  spiders' success,
But she thought she'd be firm with them
  nevertheless;
She gave them fresh orders but they
  said with a sneer,
"You're history – now spiders give
  orders round here!"

They threw Hayley out. She'd five
   minutes to pack,
And she left the house shouting, "Just
   wait, I'll be back!"
But they were too busy devising a plan
To spread through the world and take
   over from Man.

So when next a big spider crawls out
   of your plug,
Don't turn on the tap with a smile
   and a shrug,
To be swilled down the drain makes
   them awfully vexed,
You should always remember,
   YOUR HOUSE MIGHT BE NEXT...

David Orme

Colonel Fazackerley

Colonel Fazackerley Butterworth-Toast
Bought an old castle complete with
    a ghost,
But someone or other forgot to declare
To Colonel Fazack that the spectre
    was there.

On the very first evening, while
    waiting to dine,
The Colonel was taking a fine
    sherry wine,
When the ghost, with a furious flash
    and a flare,
Shot out of the chimney and shivered,
    "Beware!"

Colonel Fazackerley put down his glass
And said, "My dear fellow, that's really
   first class!
I just can't conceive how you do it at all.
I imagine you're going to a Fancy
   Dress Ball?"

At this, the dread ghost gave a
    withering cry.
Said the Colonel (his monocle firm in
    his eye),
"Now just how you do it I wish I
    could think.
Do sit down and tell me, and please
    have a drink."

The ghost in his phosphorous cloak
gave a roar
And floated about between ceiling
and floor.
He walked through a wall and returned
through a pane
And backed up the chimney and came
down again.

Said the Colonel, "With laughter I'm
   feeling quite weak!"
(As trickles of merriment ran down
   his cheek).
"My house-warming party I hope you
   won't spurn.
You *must* say you'll come and you'll
   give us a turn!"

At this, the poor spectre – quite out
　of his wits –
Proceeded to shake himself almost
　to bits.
He rattled his chains and he clattered
　his bones
And he filled the whole castle with
　mumbles and moans.

But Colonel Fazackerley, just as before,

Was simply delighted and called out,
   "Encore!"

At which the ghost vanished, his efforts
   in vain,

And never was seen at the castle again.

"Oh dear, what a pity!"
   said Colonel Fazack.
"I don't know his name, so I can't call
   him back."
And then with a smile that was hard
   to define,
Colonel Fazackerley went in to dine.

Charles Causley

A Life

You were born in January, with the
  year as white
as the paper you're writing on, at dead
  of night.

You remembered your cradle and the
  wooden hood
where the snow came drifting as we
  knew it would.

You toddled in March on the windy sand
in nappies and knickers and anorak and

in April you hoped school would be OK
and the bustling bullies wouldn't come
   your way.

In May dressed up in a blazer, black,
you gazed like the moon at the
   railway track

which took you in June to Dylan Street,
holes in the soles of the shoes on
    your feet.

July, and you'd found
    a passable way
to earn a living
    day by day.

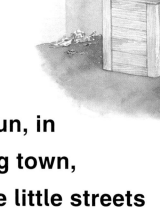

Under foreign sun, in
    the sweltering town,
you dawdled the little streets
    up and down.

In late September at a football game
you chanted a boyish hero's name.

In October at Colinsford Fair
you swung on a ship on a wing and
   a prayer.

November came as you pulled at
   your hood
by a bonfire crazed with flame and wood.

It's December, and the year's as white
as the paper you're writing on at dead
   of night.

Fred Sedgwick

The Listeners

"Is there anybody there?" said
    the Traveller,
Knocking on the moonlit door;
And his horse in the silence
    champed the grasses
Of the forest's ferny floor:
And a bird flew up out of the turret,
Above the Traveller's head;
And he smote upon the door
    a second time;
"Is there anybody there?" he said.

But no one descended to the Traveller;
No head from the leaf-fringed sill
Leaned over and looked into his grey eyes,
Where he stood perplexed and still.

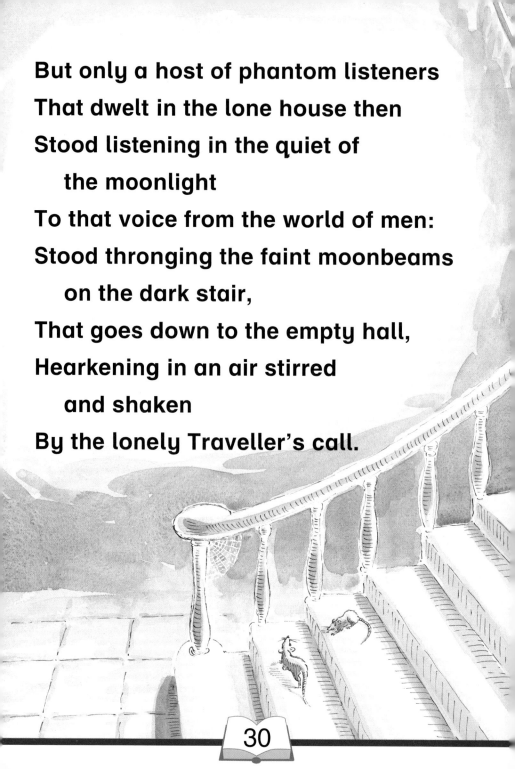

But only a host of phantom listeners
That dwelt in the lone house then
Stood listening in the quiet of
   the moonlight
To that voice from the world of men:
Stood thronging the faint moonbeams
   on the dark stair,
That goes down to the empty hall,
Hearkening in an air stirred
   and shaken
By the lonely Traveller's call.

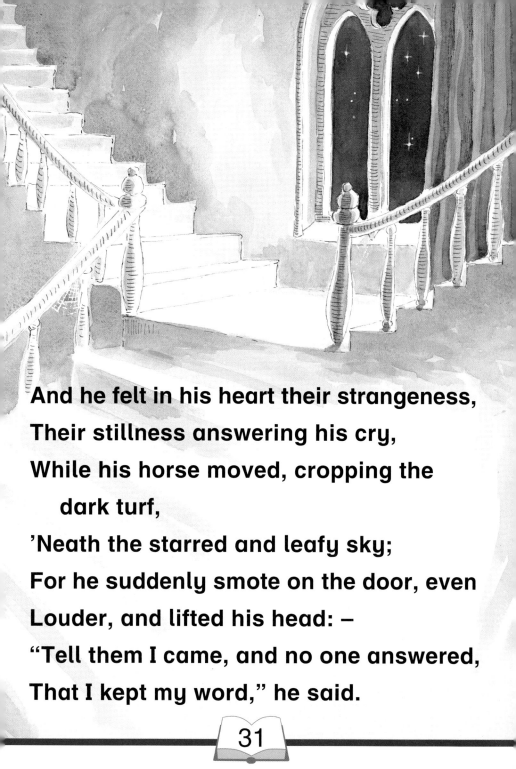

And he felt in his heart their strangeness,
Their stillness answering his cry,
While his horse moved, cropping the
   dark turf,
'Neath the starred and leafy sky;
For he suddenly smote on the door, even
Louder, and lifted his head: –
"Tell them I came, and no one answered,
That I kept my word," he said.

Never the least stir made the listeners,
Though every word he spake
Fell echoing through the shadowiness of
   the still house
From the one man left awake:
Ay, they heard his foot upon the stirrup,
And the sound of iron on stone,
And how the silence surged softly
   backward,
When the plunging hoofs were gone.

Walter de la Mare